said

Copy

by Liza Charlesworth

ISBN: 978-1-338-78281-3
Illustrated by Michael Robertson
Copyright © 2021 by Liza Charlesworth. All rights reserved.
Published by Scholastic Inc., 557 Broadway, New York, NY 10012

10 9 8 7 6 5 4 3 2 1   68   21 22 23 24 25 26 27/0

Printed in Jiaxing, China. First printing, June 2021.

Copy Cow saw Dog.
She **said** what Dog **said**.

2

Copy Cow saw Hen.
She **said** what Hen **said**.

Copy Cow saw Horse.
She **said** what Horse **said**.

4

Copy Cow saw Pig.
She **said** what Pig **said**.

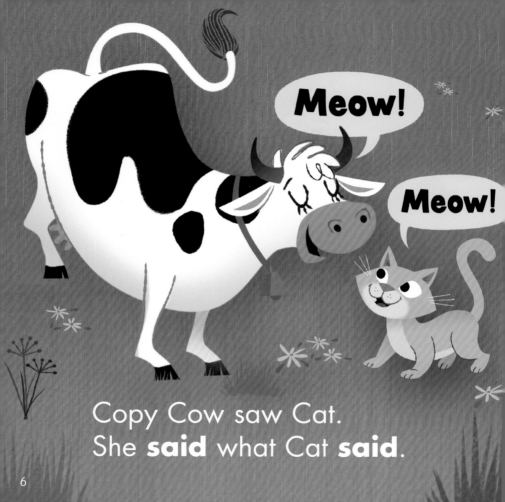

Copy Cow saw Cat.
She **said** what Cat **said**.

6

Copy Cow saw Sheep.
She **said** what Sheep **said**.

Copy Cow saw Farmer.
She **said** what Farmer **said**.